Morning Messages

Morning Messages:

6 Minutes a Day
to
The Life of Your Dreams

A Guided Journal

Michele Vosberg, Ph.D

First Printing: December 2020
ISBN: 978-1-7362273-0-5

Disclaimer:
This book is designed to provide practical and applicable content regarding the subject covered. Neither the author nor publisher is engaged in rendering legal, financial, medical or other professional advice. If expert assistance is required, the services of a professional should be sought.

Inspired Together Learning
P.O. Box 8291
3903 Milwaukee St.
Madison, WI 53708

Dare to live the life you have dreamed for yourself. Go forward and make your dreams come true.

Ralph Waldo Emerson

Chapter 1

Welcome to Your Inspired, Intentional Life

You picked up this book because you have dreams or goals and want to make them reality. You are already taking action, which tells me that you are the kind of person who is willing to do more than fantasize about living the life of your dreams. You are willing to work for it. You're my kind of person!

Some of you may be just starting out on your dream path. You don't have a solid dream yet, but you are feeling restless. You might have a yearning for something you can't quite express. You're feeling that there is something more to life than your current experience, and it nags at you. Maybe you want a change but feel a little guilty that your perfectly good life just isn't good enough anymore. There is something out there waiting for you, and you are willing to go after it.

On the other end of the spectrum, some of you are focused and driven, ready to create a life beyond your wildest imagination. You have a vision for your life, and you are ready to take action. Maybe you already have a big dream but haven't made it happen yet.

You dare to dream of something more, something different, something better.

I'm excited for you!

Most dreams start with a whisper, a small thought, or a nagging sense that there is something else for you, something that is just on the other side if only you knew how to get it.

Those whispers are your true self, your inner wisdom guiding you. Your inner wisdom is genius, and if you can learn to listen to it and trust it, it will serve you well.

What you are feeling is potential, and it is fueled by passion and purpose. The exciting thing is that *where there is potential, there is possibility and when you believe that things are possible, you can take the steps needed to make them happen.*

We are given our hopes and dreams for a reason; we are supposed to fulfill them. Potential wants to be born. It wants us to be successful, alive and fulfilled in every area of our lives.

Bringing potential to life is not always an easy and straightforward process. You probably have doubts. How can I make my dream come true when I don't even know how to do it? Who am I to achieve these audacious dreams? You might have tried and failed at things that were important to you, which leaves you feeling doubtful or even hopeless.

We all have struggles. Despite the images we see on Instagram and Facebook, there is no perfectly charmed life. Rather than be discouraged and frustrated by our challenges, we can recognize them and combat them. We can choose to refuse to let them control our destiny. We can act *in spite of* our challenges.

Dreams Fulfilled: How this Process was Born

The process that I am sharing with you in this journal is one that works. I know because I have used it over and over again to make my dreams come to life. It started when I was seventeen years old and had a dream and didn't know how I would ever make it happen.

I've always been a dreamer. As a child, I loved to read. I learned through books that there were lives and worlds other than my own. Reading became a doorway for me to explore and dream and ultimately was crucial to fulfilling my own dreams.

In my world, there wasn't a lot of support for big dreams.

My family survived by being practical and hard working. I was the oldest of five children and my mother ran a home daycare. There was always a baby to feed, a diaper to change, dishes to be washed or something to vacuum. When I would sneak away to read, I was often told, "get your nose out of that book."

By the time I was twelve, I cooked dinner and cared for my younger siblings when my mom went to work. By the age of thirteen I had a thriving babysitting business of my own. Those experiences taught me that you have to work hard for the things that you want.

My relatives were hardworking people who worked with their hands. They were farmers, cooks, seamstresses, carpenters and bricklayers. Being academically smart was not only not respected, it was ridiculed. Intellectuals were hoity-toity people who didn't even know how to make a decent meal or fix their own cars.

As a girl who loved learning more than anything else, this message was devastating. My dream was college, but other than my teachers and the people I read about in books, I knew very few people who had been to college. I had wonderful, loving parents, but they did not value higher education. I suspected that my family would not encourage my college dream, and I was right.

Most families have college hopes for their children, mine tried to talk me out of it. No one would have batted an eye if I had turned my part-time job at a grocery store into a full-time job. My Grandma lobbied for me to be a file clerk. The money was good and after a year or so I could get married, have a baby, and quit.

My mother, always practical, did not want me to waste my time and money on a college degree. She wanted me to get a job as a licensed practical nurse. I wouldn't need a four -year degree and I would always be assured of a job. When I protested, she found me a two-year community college program where I could earn a license as a Registered Nurse.

My father was a mid-level manager at a computer company when computers were just taking off. He had worked his way up and was proof positive that you could get a good job without wasting money on college. Most of my many cousins got jobs and got married young. I struggled to find role models or support for my college dreams.

I know now that I was born for academics. Learning is in my DNA; it is who I am and at the top of my values list. It is also one of my highest strengths. **Today I understand that when your passions and skills align with your work you are more likely to be happy, fulfilled and successful.** But back then, all I knew was that my yearning for knowledge was a core part of my being. I was desperate to go to college and I stuck to my dream like my life depended on it. And maybe it did.

With few role models, and no guidance to help me figure it out, I managed to get admitted to The University of Wisconsin. I told my parents that I was going to study nursing, although I knew I would never be a nurse. I thought that my little white lie would quiet the naysayers. I was trying to protect myself and my dream.

My parents supported me by allowing me to live at home. Every morning at 5:30 A.M. I got on a bus that would take me to campus. My first day on campus, I looked up at the dorms, which held more people than the small town I came from and was in awe. I felt like I had entered an alternate universe, one I didn't belong in, but was eager to join.

My college experience was not the usual one. As a commuter student, I had few friends. I rarely attended parties or social events.

I went to my classes, worked two or three jobs at a time, and did homework until the wee hours of the morning. Despite my struggles, I loved college and thrived. I loved being around others who were intellectually curious, appreciated ideas and valued knowledge. It was the most life affirming thing I had ever experienced.

I was relentless -nothing was going to get in my way of my dream.

Achieving my dream of attending and eventually graduating from college taught me that despite the challenges, I could have what my heart most desired. It was a powerful lesson in dream fulfillment.

Going to college was the first of many dreams that I made come true. I learned that fighting for my dreams was worth it. Achieving dreams became a way of life. I went after and achieved new dreams. As I made changes in my life, I could always see new possibilities, new things that excited me and made me anxious to get out of bed in the morning. Life is never dull when you are chasing things you are passionate about.

I know that if you have a dream deep in your heart that is left unfulfilled, you will be better off if you allow yourself to chase it. Regret is a fierce villain.

When you go after your dreams, the end may turn out differently than you originally thought, but there is joy in the process. The United States Declaration of Independence tells us that we have the right to "Life, Liberty and the pursuit of Happiness." What is working for our dreams about if not the pursuit of happiness?

We Need a Process and a Plan

I've met many people who are struggling. They are searching for something but aren't sure how to find it. Or, they have dreams and goals but can't stay motivated to complete them.

What they need, and what we *all* need, is a process and a plan.

We need to clarify our vision and connect it to our larger purpose in life.

We need to create projects and plans to take action.

We need to learn to defy the obstacles and challenges that are in our way.

So many people start out with good intentions only to find their dreams pushed off to the side like the unused exercise equipment that now holds yesterday's clothes. Some people give up, others hold onto their dreams for someday.

This is your someday. We are not guaranteed a long life. We are not even guaranteed tomorrow. It is time to pursue your heart's desires.

I am not going to tell you it is *easy*. If it was *easy*, everyone would have everything they have ever dreamed of. What I can tell you is that it is *possible*. I believe that we CAN make our dreams come true.

We need a process and a plan. Along the way, we are also going to need regular dose of inspiration and motivation. And most importantly, **we need to keep our dreams in front of us and take small actions towards our dreams every day**. That is what the journal in the second half of this book is about.

This book can help you achieve your dreams. It isn't magic, but it works.

Curious?

Let's get going!

Chapter 2

The Process and the Plan

Most of us have dreams. Why don't we all achieve them?

Chances are some of the vital elements of dream fulfillment are missing. The first of those important elements is having a clear and compelling vision.

If you can't visualize your dream, how are you going to make it come true?

Develop a Clear and Compelling Vision.

What is your dream? Can you see it, hear it, smell it and even feel it? Can you describe it? When you close your eyes can you bring it into your mind, allowing it to wash over you and fill you with warmth and happiness?

Most evenings before I fall asleep, I think about who I want to be and what I want my world to be like. I close my eyes and imagine things I want to create, places I want to go, and people I want to be with.

These feelings make me feel calm and content. They make my dreams feel real and keep them close. They are clear and detailed and specific. I imagine my dreams as if I am watching a movie of my life.

I have often experienced a real-life version of something that started as a dream, imagined in the dark of night as I create visions of who I want to be and what I want to have in my life.

For years I had a very clear vision of myself speaking in front of a large crowd. I was standing on the stage wearing a blue suit. As I looked out, I could see hundreds of people, lined up in rows, waiting for me to talk.

When I became part of a leadership team that started a national organization, I was invited to give a speech at their convention. I found myself standing on stage, in my blue suit. As I looked through the glaring spot lights out into an audience of a thousand people, I remember thinking to myself, *I've lived this moment in my dreams.*

I imagined myself sitting in a college classroom, surrounded by other students, listening to my professors and eagerly engaging in discussions. I'd have a blue backpack, holding all of my books and notebooks, slung on one shoulder or sitting on the floor next to me.

I imagined walking across the stage at my Ph.D. ceremony, wearing the academic doctoral gown with three blue stripes on the sleeve. I'd have a fluffy beret with a gold tassel, the kind reserved for doctors. I imagined a brass medal hanging on a wide ribbon and the way I bowed my head so they could place it around my neck.

Long before I lived in my current house, I imagined living in a house near a lake, walking down to the beach with my husband to watch the sunset. We'd walk out on to the pier and sit, listening to the waves and watching the ducks while we sipped a glass of wine.

Vague dreams don't lead to passionate pursuit. You have to be able to imagine every detail.

If your dream lacks clarity, spend some time creating a vision.
To create a clear vision, ask yourself the following questions:

If I could describe my dream day, what would I be doing? Who would I be with? Where would I be?

What kind of feelings do I want to experience on a daily basis?

What do I love about my current life?

What would I like to change about my current life?

Where am I trying to fulfill someone else's dreams for me? Where am I being true to myself?

What do I love to do?

What am I passionate about?

Don't get caught up in the world of fantasy. A fantasy is something that could never happen, despite your effort. For example, as a middle-aged woman with two artificial knees, I can't dream myself into winning a gold medal as an Olympic gymnast. There are certainly aspects of that life and world I *could* create, but unless someone develops a time machine that can make me seventeen years old again, that dream is a fantasy.

How do you know if what you wish for is a fantasy? Some fantasies require a miracle such as winning the lottery. If your dream is to win a billion dollars in the lottery, it is a fantasy. There is nothing you can do to control the outcome of the lottery.

Other fantasies require a hero to swoop in and save you or give you your dream life. Yes, it has happened that a photographer discovers a young girl on the streets, recognizes her beauty and turns her into a supermodel. However, the odds that someone will magically appear and make you rich and famous are not good. If you are waiting for someone else to magically change your life, you might be in for a very long wait.

If a dream feels important, but looks like a fantasy, ask yourself what it is that the fantasy would give you. What feelings are you going after? Chances are there is a way to get those feelings in an attainable way.

This is not meant to discourage big dreams. My little girl self would not have dared to dream the things I have achieved. Dreams are attainable. They don't require a miracle or a hero. They come true with a strategy, *a strategy that **you** can control.*

When I conduct workshops and ask people to describe their dream life, many people describe sitting in a lounge chair on the beach drinking Margaritas. That is their "dream" life. It may be possible to design a life where that is the end result. I have a friend who is a successful entrepreneur who created her own business and moved to the beach in Mexico.

However, I suspect that after a couple of weeks, sitting around doing nothing would not feel very satisfying. What are you really after? More time to relax? More freedom in your schedule? More time with loved ones? More time outdoors in the sunshine and fresh air? Maybe you hate your job and want to get out from under the stress that it is causing. Those things are very attainable.

To successfully go after something you want, you have to know what it is. Create a compelling vision. Imagine all the details. Make dream boards. Create a dream wall. Close your eyes every night and call to mind every bit of your dream.

It's fun to dream, but you can't stop there. Having a compelling vision is just the first step.

Connect to Your Purpose

The word "purpose" scares people. It seems big and important, and many people fear they don't know their purpose.

Your purpose isn't a thing. It isn't an inspiration that lands on your head, like a divine gift from the purpose fairies. It isn't something you find. Purpose has been held up as the holy grail of your life. If you don't know your purpose or are holding off on creating your dreams until you discover your purpose, I have good news for you.

You don't *need* to discover your purpose. Your purpose is already there.

Your purpose is about who you are at your very core. Your purpose is in your beliefs and your values. It is in your talents and gifts. It is found in what you love and what you are good at.

Ask yourself, who am I? Start with your name. Write it down. Then write down everything that defines who you are. List your relationships, your skills and your values. Keep writing.

Then look at what you have written. Chances are that there is a nugget or two that gets at the heart and soul of who you are.

Here is my own example:
I am a reader and writer. I am skilled at taking in knowledge, synthesizing it and then making is easy to understand. I am a teacher at heart. I value sharing knowledge. I am happiest when learning and growing. I want to set an example as someone who is wise, inspired, gracious and centered.

Here is an example from a friend:
I have a deep relationship with God. I cherish helping others to understand God and live in God's path. I want to live my values with my family and friends as we continue to grow in our faith.

Here is another example:
I live for adventure. I am happiest doing things. I want to meet others from all over the world and develop abiding friendships. I love to connect with people. My work plans always revolve around saving money for my next adventure.

What is important to you? My life coach quit her practice to take a job with an organization that works to stop human trafficking. I have a friend who is very dedicated to political work and spends much of her time campaigning for people and causes she believes in. Another friend just sailed around the *entire world* in a small ship.

Maybe your purpose revolves around something less global. Maybe your most important purpose is being a good parent or being a good grandparent to your grandchildren. You might want to foster dogs, or volunteer at an animal shelter.

Still stuck? Try writing your own obituary. What do you want people in the future to say about you? What would you be proud to have done? What would you write on your tombstone?

Another helpful activity will give you some input. Text ten friends and ask them what they believe your strengths and gifts are. When I did that, I found it to be very powerful. People knew the real me, the one I didn't realize that they knew, and validated what I thought was true about myself. It was empowering.

Whatever you choose to be or do, your purpose is what will drive you. It must be important enough that you are willing to do the hard work and sacrifice for it.

When you find yourself losing motivation, investigate the reasons behind what you are doing. Ask yourself, "Why am I doing this?" You will never be motivated to do the hard work of making a dream come true if it isn't something you care about deeply.

Too often, people rely on extrinsic motivation to keep them going. Rewards such as praise, fame, or money often work in the short term. So do punishments. Intrinsic motivation, however, works much better over the long term. Intrinsic motivation, an internally held passion, will drive you to take action towards your dreams.

Newspaper columnist Sydney J. Harris once commented that your life's true work is that which you would be willing to do for free if you could afford to.

What would you be willing to do for free if you could afford to? That is your purpose.

Devise a Plan.

I'd be willing to bet that you already know a lot about planning. You have certainly experienced success in planning something. You already know about breaking down a plan into smaller, actionable steps. You've created task lists and timelines. You've created to-do lists and scheduled things in your calendar.

I'm not going to teach you how to plan. If you don't know, there are plenty of books and other resources that can teach you.

What I am going to suggest is that you treat your dreams like a project at work or a major household project and create a plan. If you love planning, as I do, this will be fun. If you dislike planning, consider it a necessary evil that will lead to you getting whatever it is you want.

> "By failing to prepare, you are preparing to fail."
>
> Benjamin Franklin

Look at the big picture of your dreams. It might seem huge and overwhelming. You might not know where to start- this is where some people quit.

But you are smarter than that. Remember, you already know how to plan.

Take the big audacious dream and start breaking it down. Look for the projects that you will need to accomplish before you achieve your dream.

For example, if your dream is to take a year's leave of absence from your job and spend a year living abroad, look for the projects. You might have a financial project which includes items like saving money, finding someone to rent out your home and creating a travel budget. You might have a location project which involves investigating all of the possibly places you might live and then narrowing it down to a specific region and securing a place to live. Another project might involve finding and attending classes to become more proficient in the language of the country where you to plan to move.

Give each project a folder and a name. Continue to break down each project to smaller and smaller pieces. As new ideas or new steps come up, add them to the folder.

Planning to move abroad for a year might sound overwhelming. Where do you even start? Once you break it down into doable pieces, it becomes less formidable. Picking up the phone to inquire about taking a course to learn Portuguese is simple. Fill your project folders with simple steps. Make the steps small enough that they don't scare you.

Once you have little steps, you are well on your way. Don't get overwhelmed by the enormity of the task. Tackle one project at a time. Do one step, then another.

In the television comedy *Mash,* there is a character named Corporal Klinger who engages in crazy plots and schemes so he will be declared mentally unfit and sent home. In one episode, he decides to eat a jeep.

It is a ridiculous undertaking, and you wouldn't want to do it. How in the world could that even be possible?

Klinger breaks the jeep down into tiny pieces and starts to eat it one lug nut at a time.

That is how you get to your dream. One bite at a time.

Still overwhelmed? Don't worry, I'll help you find your plan and keep updating it as you complete the journal in the second half of this book.

Take Consistent Action.

As the old saying goes, Rome wasn't built in a day. Neither is a dream. If you can accomplish your dream in one day, you aren't dreaming big enough!

We all wish we had more time to work on our dreams. Are you waiting until you have more time? Are you hoping to finish all your current projects so you can start working on your dream project? Are you planning to start your dream project when you retire?

That is not how dreams are made real.

Think about something that you have achieved in your life. How long did it take? Did you apply for a job, interview for a job and start a new job in a week? It's doubtful. Did you meet the love of your life, get married and raise a family in a week? Of course not!

Good things can take time to come to fruition. This is not meant to discourage you, but if you are waiting until you have all the time in the world, you might be missing the boat.

If you are serious about your dream, you are going to need to find some time and get started.

You have already created a plan. You've broken down your projects into the smallest of bites- something that takes minutes or an hour at most. Looking at an overwhelming task is intimidating. Now is the time to take control.

Pick one small thing and do it. Schedule it into your day. Do it and *cross it off the list.* Then do the next thing and *cross it off the list.* It feels satisfying to cross things off the list. Those of you who write things you've already done on your to-do list just so you can cross them off already understand this!

When you get stuck and don't know which thing to do next- find something you can do and do it.

Do not let two days in a row go without doing something, however small, that will move you closer to fulfilling your dream. With small, consistent action, you will make progress. Taking action also builds momentum.

Don't throw away your lists. Keep them there to remind you of your accomplishments. It is satisfying to look at a list and see all the progress you have made. When you are struggling with the next step, remind yourself how far you have already come, rather than how far you still need to go.

As you complete more and more pieces and see progress, you will want to take even more action. If you never want to do any work to achieve your dreams, you might need to go back to the beginning and rethink your dream.

Challenge Your Gremlins

There are always obstacles on the path of life. This is true whether or not you are pursuing your dreams. **Life hands us some of those obstacles, others are of our own making. Either way they can derail us. Sometimes they even make us quit.**

Life's obstacles include things we often can't control such as accidents, illness, death of a loved one, loss of a job, and most recently, the pandemic. We may not be able to control or prevent the outcome, but we can control how we react to it. These things require time, support, and resiliency. They may slow you down or stop you for a time. That is to be expected.

The gremlins in our heads are even more likely to stop us in our tracks. Our gremlins may be things we learned in childhood or have generalized from our own experiences. They may be deeply ingrained in our value systems. They may slow us down or sabotage us forever if we let them. Here are some examples:

Fear of failure
Fear of judgement
Guilt
Comparison
Perfectionism
Money issues
Imposter syndrome
Fear of success

These are the gremlins that are most likely to appear as we follow our dreams. The closer we get, the louder they roar. They are trying to protect us in the best way they know how which is to shut us down. They keep us safe by instilling fear. When something is new and unknown, fear is natural. We've learned to respect fear and pay attention. It keeps us safe and alive.

We do need to pay attention. But we also need to recognize when fear is irrational, when it not only isn't protecting us, but is hindering us. When one of our fears is not serving us, we need to challenge it.

How do you challenge a gremlin? Here are some suggestions:

Change your self-talk. Ask, what am I saying to myself? Is it true? What is the evidence that it is or isn't true? Is it is coming from a past negative experience? If so, what is different this time?

Recognize where the voice is coming from. Is the voice from your childhood? Your boss? Is it your emotional brain talking or your rational brain talking?

Consider the danger. What is the gremlin warning you about? Is it a real danger? What can you do to mitigate potential danger?

Talk back. Tell your gremlin the truth. Imagine your gremlin is telling you not to do something because you might lose all of your money. You answer back, "Yes, I know you are worried that I won't have enough money, but I would like to remind you that I have always been a good steward of my money and I will be this time as well."

Be careful who you share your dreams with. Don't let others belittle your ambitions. Your dreams are sacred. Not everyone will be supportive and that is okay, you don't need everyone to be on board. If your gremlin is afraid that others will judge you, don't share your plans with the judgers. Instead, surround yourself with people who will champion your dream.

Stop comparing yourself to others. Comparison is the thief of joy. You have your own process and will work in your own time. Consider where your comparisons are coming from. Turn off your social media. Stop looking at perfected photos in glossy magazines. Be especially careful of comparing yourself to others who are further along on their path.

Stop living to fulfill others' expectations. Your journey is your own. Being who others expect you to be is not the way to fulfill your own dreams. Have some honest conversations with people in your life. Your needs matter, and you will be a better son, daughter, partner, friend, parent, or worker when your own needs are met.

Stop trying to be "balanced." What does balanced mean to you? Balance does not mean everything in your life gets equal time. It means that each thing gets the time that it needs at the moment.

Stay out of what is not yours. Focus on *your* concerns, worries, responsibilities. Stop trying to fix or control everyone else.

Adopt a growth mindset rather than a fixed mindset. A growth mindset recognizes that people always grow and change. Mistakes are just part of the process and you learn from them. Mistakes are to be expected, not feared.

Believe you can have your dream. Don't worry if you don't yet know how. You can get help when you need it and you can learn along the way.

When you are on the path to your dreams, your gremlins are bound to pop up. When they do, stop and say hello. Get to know the enemy so you can be prepared for the challenges.

Living with Intention

How do you want to show up in the world? Who do you want to be? How do you want to act?

In the past few years, many people have replaced New Year's resolution with a word of the year. A word for the year summarizes how you want to be, what you want to feel, or how you want to live. It sets your intention for the year.

We don't need to wait until December in order to set our intention. Who says we are only allowed one word? We can set an intention every day for how we want to be or feel or live that day. We can even choose a different word every day!

Make a list of words that define how you want to be in the world. These are words that describe you at your best. How would you be or feel if you were living every day fully engaged, joyful, and with confidence?

Keep your list handy and refer to it as you answer the questions in this journal. Taking a moment to jot a word claiming your intention for the day will keep you on the path towards living with intention.

We all have our own life to pursue,

our own kind of dream to be weaving,

and we all have the power

to make our wishes come true,

as long as we keep believing.

Louisa May Alcott

Chapter 3

How to Use This Journal

This book is a guided journal. The rest of the pages are for your work. They are specifically designed to guide your process. Each of the questions has a purpose and connects to one of the things that you will need to do in order to achieve your dream.

This process doesn't require a lot of time. You can complete the questions in just a few minutes in the beginning of the day. Make it a ritual. Find a comfy place to sit and grab your coffee, cup of tea or green smoothie.

Take a few minutes to write your reflection. Pay attention to the good things and the good moments. Focusing on the positive things in your world helps your stay positive. This process can also be done in just a few minutes- or if you love journaling and love to take time with your thoughts you can write more.

Understanding the reason behind each question will help you stay motivated. Let's look at the rationale for each of the questions.

Question 1

Vision: What feelings or experiences would you like to have had by the end of today?

Just like Olympic athletes who visualize their gold medal winning run, *you need keep your eyes on the prize*. There is research that proves that our mind cannot distinguish between thoughts that are about things you have experienced and thoughts that you are imagining. Your mind believes what you tell it. The more realistic and life-like you can make your visions, the more real they will seem to your brain.

What we see in our mind is what we get in our life.

You may have heard the phrase *you've got to believe it to achieve it.* Visualize what you want to achieve. Think about the feelings and experiences you want to have and write them down. You will be reminding yourself how you want to be and live in the world.

Question 2

Motivation: What would my best self like to say to me today?

We've all struggled with motivation from time-to-time. We know we should do something, but we can't quite make ourselves do it. We start strong but fizzle out.

You have probably heard a lot of advice about motivation. Get an accountability partner. Reward yourself when you accomplish something. Punish yourself when you don't follow through. Set up a competition with another person. Some of these ideas will work for you, others won't.

Just like with underwear, motivation is not a one size fits all proposition. There is no one way to motivate everyone. You need to understand what motivates *you*. Do you work well with a drill sergeant like voice screaming at you to "step it up?" or does that voice fill you with terror and make you shut down? Do you enjoy a kind gentle voice reminding you of your goals, and encouraging you to take care of yourself, or does that lead you to the sofa with a bag of chips?

What would you like to hear? You have an inner coach. Your inner coach is the best version of yourself. This person is wise and understands you very well. Your inner coach knows how to guide you. Let your inner coach be the voice in your ear.

The problem isn't your lack of motivation, it is the regular renewal of your motivation. Question 2 is designed to bring you a regular dose of inner motivation. Let your wise inner coach remind you of who you want to be and what you want to do every single day.

Question 3

Planning: What are my three priorities for today?

You are more likely to make progress when you plan your actions rather than leaving them to happenstance.

Choose the most important three things you want to get done each day, and then and set the intention to accomplish at least those three things. This will make sure you are working on the things that are important to you.

Your three things will undoubtedly include things you must do for your job, your family, or other obligations. You also have an obligation to yourself. Make sure that the projects in your dream plans show up here too.

Question 4:

Action: What is one small action I can take today that will bring me closer to my goals and dreams?

Look at the task lists that you have created in your dream project files. **Make sure that you do at least one task, however small that moves you forward towards your dreams.** Consistency is the key- small tasks done regularly add up to real progress.

Question 5

Challenges: What obstacles, challenges, or mindset issues might I have to overcome today? What can I do to minimize them?

This question allows you to face your gremlins head on. You will always have obstacles in your path, but knowing this, you can plan for them. Which of your gremlins might be particularly important right now? This question gives you a chance to talk back, to defend yourself, to be proactive and to face your fears with courage.

Question 6

Live with Intention: My word of the day is _____.

On page 36 you will create a list of words that describe how you want to be. Think about your plans for the day and all of the things you will do. Think of the people you will interact with. Think of the challenges you might experience. Then assign a word that will remind you of how you want to face the world today.

Is this your day to be bold? Brave? Curious? Kindhearted? Loving? Gracious? Focused?

Name it and it is yours. You have set your intention for the day.

Reflection Question

As I think about my thoughts, feelings and actions, what feels satisfying in my world? How am I aligning my purpose, passion, projects and performance to help me achieve my dreams?

On the back of each question page is a reflection page. This is an open-ended page designed to give you a space to record your thoughts and feelings. This page will help you feel grateful as you recognize the positive things in your life. It is also an opportunity to celebrate small wins, and to acknowledge how you showed up for yourself in ways that make you proud.

You can do this page in the morning as a way to stay centered and focused. If you are short of time in the morning, you can also do it in the evening. I sometimes complete this page just before I go to bed each night, which leaves me reflecting on the good things in my life before I fall asleep.

Making your dreams come true can be a long process. Sometimes you will feel alone, or that no one is pulling for you. You have to be rooting for yourself. You have to acknowledge just what you are capable of and give yourself credit for all that you are doing.

These pages will keep you honest and urge you to keep going. Something magic happens when you dare to dream, make a plan and slowly but surely, take action.

> Magic is believing in yourself.
> If you can do that, you can make anything happen.
>
> Johann Wolfgang von Goethe

We *can* bring our dreams to life. We need to stay connected to our vision, stay motivated, stay inspired and stay focused. We need to create the plans and projects that will lead us to achieving our goals and dreams.

The things you focus your attention on grow. This book is designed to help you keep your dreams in front of you every day, to make you think and act in ways that will move you forward.

A dream deferred is a dream lost. You can't wait until someday to make your dreams happen, you have to start now, and you have to move with intention. You don't have to have all the answers or know all the steps. You just need to start listening to yourself, and taking small, purposeful actions. Your guided journal will help you to stay connected to your dream and stay focused on your plans. It will help you to create your own best future.

This is intentional living.

If you want something you have never had,
you must be willing to do something
you have never done.

Thomas Jefferson

Part Two

Your Journal

What dreams would I like to bring to life? What is my vision? What details can I describe that will make my dream seem clear?

Use this space to write or draw your ideas.

Why is this dream important to me? What values, skills, interests and passions can I bring together to reinforce my motivation to work towards this dream?

Use this space to write or draw your ideas.

What are the projects that I will need to work on as I work toward my dream?

Use this space to write or draw your ideas.

What are some challenges or obstacles that might keep me from achieving my dream?

Use this space to write or draw your ideas.

What are some words that will help me live with intention? How would my best self act? How do I want to think, feel and act as I work on the life of my dreams?

Use this space to write or draw your ideas.

The future belongs to those
who believe in the beauty
of their dreams.

Eleanor Roosevelt

Morning Messages

Vision: What feelings or experiences would you like to have had by the end of today?

_____

_____

_____

Motivation: What would my best self like to say to me today?

_____

_____

_____

Planning: What are my three priorities for today?

_____

_____

_____

Action: What is one small action I can take today that will bring me closer to my goals and dreams?

_____

_____

_____

Challenges: What obstacles, challenges, or mindset issues might I have to overcome today? What can I do to minimize them?

_____

_____

_____

Live with Intention: My word of the day is _____.

Reflection

As I think about my thoughts, feelings and actions, what feels satisfying in my world? How am I aligning my purpose, passion, projects and performance to help me achieve my dreams?

_____

_____

_____

_____

_____

_____

_____

_____

_____

_____

_____

_____

_____

_____

_____

_____

_____

_____

_____

Morning Messages

Vision: What feelings or experiences would you like to have had by the end of today?

_____

_____

_____

Motivation: What would my best self like to say to me today?

_____

_____

_____

Planning: What are my three priorities for today?

_____

_____

_____

Action: What is one small action I can take today that will bring me closer to my goals and dreams?

_____

_____

_____

Challenges: What obstacles, challenges, or mindset issues might I have to overcome today? What can I do to minimize them?

_____

_____

_____

Live with Intention: My word of the day is _____.

Reflection

As I think about my thoughts, feelings and actions, what feels satisfying in my world? How am I aligning my purpose, passion, projects and performance to help me achieve my dreams?

_____

_____

_____

_____

_____

_____

_____

_____

_____

_____

_____

_____

_____

_____

_____

_____

_____

_____

_____

_____

Morning Messages

Vision: What feelings or experiences would you like to have had by the end of today?

_____

_____

_____

Motivation: What would my best self like to say to me today?

_____

_____

_____

Planning: What are my three priorities for today?

_____

_____

_____

Action: What is one small action I can take today that will bring me closer to my goals and dreams?

_____

_____

_____

Challenges: What obstacles, challenges, or mindset issues might I have to overcome today? What can I do to minimize them?

_____

_____

_____

Live with Intention: My word of the day is _____.

Reflection

As I think about my thoughts, feelings and actions, what feels satisfying in my world? How am I aligning my purpose, passion, projects and performance to help me achieve my dreams?

Morning Messages

Vision: What feelings or experiences would you like to have had by the end of today?

_____

_____

_____

Motivation: What would my best self like to say to me today?

_____

_____

_____

Planning: What are my three priorities for today?

_____

_____

_____

Action: What is one small action I can take today that will bring me closer to my goals and dreams?

_____

_____

_____

Challenges: What obstacles, challenges, or mindset issues might I have to overcome today? What can I do to minimize them?

_____

_____

_____

Live with Intention: My word of the day is _____.

Reflection

As I think about my thoughts, feelings and actions, what feels satisfying in my world? How am I aligning my purpose, passion, projects and performance to help me achieve my dreams?

_____

_____

_____

_____

_____

_____

_____

_____

_____

_____

_____

_____

_____

_____

_____

_____

_____

_____

_____

Morning Messages

Vision: What feelings or experiences would you like to have had by the end of today?

_____

_____

_____

Motivation: What would my best self like to say to me today?

_____

_____

_____

Planning: What are my three priorities for today?

_____

_____

_____

Action: What is one small action I can take today that will bring me closer to my goals and dreams?

_____

_____

_____

Challenges: What obstacles, challenges, or mindset issues might I have to overcome today? What can I do to minimize them?

_____

_____

_____

Live with Intention: My word of the day is _____.

Reflection

As I think about my thoughts, feelings and actions, what feels satisfying in my world? How am I aligning my purpose, passion, projects and performance to help me achieve my dreams?

_____

_____

_____

_____

_____

_____

_____

_____

_____

_____

_____

_____

_____

_____

_____

_____

_____

_____

_____

_____

Morning Messages

Vision: What feelings or experiences would you like to have had by the end of today?

_____

_____

_____

Motivation: What would my best self like to say to me today?

_____

_____

_____

Planning: What are my three priorities for today?

_____

_____

_____

Action: What is one small action I can take today that will bring me closer to my goals and dreams?

_____

_____

_____

Challenges: What obstacles, challenges, or mindset issues might I have to overcome today? What can I do to minimize them?

_____

_____

_____

Live with Intention: My word of the day is _____.

Reflection

As I think about my thoughts, feelings and actions, what feels satisfying in my world? How am I aligning my purpose, passion, projects and performance to help me achieve my dreams?

_____

_____

_____

_____

_____

_____

_____

_____

_____

_____

_____

_____

_____

_____

_____

_____

_____

_____

_____

_____

_____

Morning Messages

Vision: What feelings or experiences would you like to have had by the end of today?

_____

_____

_____

Motivation: What would my best self like to say to me today?

_____

_____

_____

Planning: What are my three priorities for today?

_____

_____

_____

Action: What is one small action I can take today that will bring me closer to my goals and dreams?

_____

_____

_____

Challenges: What obstacles, challenges, or mindset issues might I have to overcome today? What can I do to minimize them?

_____

_____

_____

Live with Intention: My word of the day is _____.

Reflection

As I think about my thoughts, feelings and actions, what feels satisfying in my world? How am I aligning my purpose, passion, projects and performance to help me achieve my dreams?

_____

_____

_____

_____

_____

_____

_____

_____

_____

_____

_____

_____

_____

_____

_____

_____

_____

_____

_____

_____

_____

Morning Messages

Vision: What feelings or experiences would you like to have had by the end of today?

_____

_____

_____

Motivation: What would my best self like to say to me today?

_____

_____

_____

Planning: What are my three priorities for today?

_____

_____

_____

Action: What is one small action I can take today that will bring me closer to my goals and dreams?

_____

_____

_____

Challenges: What obstacles, challenges, or mindset issues might I have to overcome today? What can I do to minimize them?

_____

_____

_____

Live with Intention: My word of the day is _____.

Reflection

As I think about my thoughts, feelings and actions, what feels satisfying in my world? How am I aligning my purpose, passion, projects and performance to help me achieve my dreams?

_____

_____

_____

_____

_____

_____

_____

_____

_____

_____

_____

_____

_____

_____

_____

_____

_____

_____

_____

_____

Morning Messages

Vision: What feelings or experiences would you like to have had by the end of today?

_____

_____

_____

Motivation: What would my best self like to say to me today?

_____

_____

_____

Planning: What are my three priorities for today?

_____

_____

_____

Action: What is one small action I can take today that will bring me closer to my goals and dreams?

_____

_____

_____

Challenges: What obstacles, challenges, or mindset issues might I have to overcome today? What can I do to minimize them?

_____

_____

_____

Live with Intention: My word of the day is _____.

Reflection

As I think about my thoughts, feelings and actions, what feels satisfying in my world? How am I aligning my purpose, passion, projects and performance to help me achieve my dreams?

_____

_____

_____

_____

_____

_____

_____

_____

_____

_____

_____

_____

_____

_____

_____

_____

_____

_____

_____

_____

_____

_____

Morning Messages

Vision: What feelings or experiences would you like to have had by the end of today?

_____

_____

_____

Motivation: What would my best self like to say to me today?

_____

_____

_____

Planning: What are my three priorities for today?

_____

_____

_____

Action: What is one small action I can take today that will bring me closer to my goals and dreams?

_____

_____

_____

Challenges: What obstacles, challenges, or mindset issues might I have to overcome today? What can I do to minimize them?

_____

_____

_____

Live with Intention: My word of the day is _____.

Reflection

As I think about my thoughts, feelings and actions, what feels satisfying in my world? How am I aligning my purpose, passion, projects and performance to help me achieve my dreams?

_____

_____

_____

_____

_____

_____

_____

_____

_____

_____

_____

_____

_____

_____

_____

_____

_____

_____

Morning Messages

Vision: What feelings or experiences would you like to have had by the end of today?

_____

_____

_____

Motivation: What would my best self like to say to me today?

_____

_____

_____

Planning: What are my three priorities for today?

_____

_____

_____

Action: What is one small action I can take today that will bring me closer to my goals and dreams?

_____

_____

_____

Challenges: What obstacles, challenges, or mindset issues might I have to overcome today? What can I do to minimize them?

_____

_____

_____

Live with Intention: My word of the day is _____.

Reflection

As I think about my thoughts, feelings and actions, what feels satisfying in my world? How am I aligning my purpose, passion, projects and performance to help me achieve my dreams?

_____

_____

_____

_____

_____

_____

_____

_____

_____

_____

_____

_____

_____

_____

_____

_____

_____

_____

_____

Morning Messages

Vision: What feelings or experiences would you like to have had by the end of today?

_____

_____

_____

Motivation: What would my best self like to say to me today?

_____

_____

_____

Planning: What are my three priorities for today?

_____

_____

_____

Action: What is one small action I can take today that will bring me closer to my goals and dreams?

_____

_____

_____

Challenges: What obstacles, challenges, or mindset issues might I have to overcome today? What can I do to minimize them?

_____

_____

_____

Live with Intention: My word of the day is _____.

Reflection

As I think about my thoughts, feelings and actions, what feels satisfying in my world? How am I aligning my purpose, passion, projects and performance to help me achieve my dreams?

Morning Messages

Vision: What feelings or experiences would you like to have had by the end of today?

_____

_____

_____

Motivation: What would my best self like to say to me today?

_____

_____

_____

Planning: What are my three priorities for today?

_____

_____

_____

Action: What is one small action I can take today that will bring me closer to my goals and dreams?

_____

_____

_____

Challenges: What obstacles, challenges, or mindset issues might I have to overcome today? What can I do to minimize them?

_____

_____

_____

Live with Intention: My word of the day is _____.

Reflection

As I think about my thoughts, feelings and actions, what feels satisfying in my world? How am I aligning my purpose, passion, projects and performance to help me achieve my dreams?

_____

_____

_____

_____

_____

_____

_____

_____

_____

_____

_____

_____

_____

_____

_____

_____

_____

_____

_____

_____

_____

_____

Morning Messages

Vision: What feelings or experiences would you like to have had by the end of today?

_____

_____

_____

Motivation: What would my best self like to say to me today?

_____

_____

_____

Planning: What are my three priorities for today?

_____

_____

_____

Action: What is one small action I can take today that will bring me closer to my goals and dreams?

_____

_____

_____

Challenges: What obstacles, challenges, or mindset issues might I have to overcome today? What can I do to minimize them?

_____

_____

_____

Live with Intention: My word of the day is _____.

Reflection

As I think about my thoughts, feelings and actions, what feels satisfying in my world? How am I aligning my purpose, passion, projects and performance to help me achieve my dreams?

_____

_____

_____

_____

_____

_____

_____

_____

_____

_____

_____

_____

_____

_____

_____

_____

_____

_____

_____

_____

_____

Morning Messages

Vision: What feelings or experiences would you like to have had by the end of today?

_____

_____

_____

Motivation: What would my best self like to say to me today?

_____

_____

_____

Planning: What are my three priorities for today?

_____

_____

_____

Action: What is one small action I can take today that will bring me closer to my goals and dreams?

_____

_____

_____

Challenges: What obstacles, challenges, or mindset issues might I have to overcome today? What can I do to minimize them?

_____

_____

_____

Live with Intention: My word of the day is _____.

Reflection

As I think about my thoughts, feelings and actions, what feels satisfying in my world? How am I aligning my purpose, passion, projects and performance to help me achieve my dreams?

Morning Messages

Vision: What feelings or experiences would you like to have had by the end of today?

_____

_____

_____

Motivation: What would my best self like to say to me today?

_____

_____

_____

Planning: What are my three priorities for today?

_____

_____

_____

Action: What is one small action I can take today that will bring me closer to my goals and dreams?

_____

_____

_____

Challenges: What obstacles, challenges, or mindset issues might I have to overcome today? What can I do to minimize them?

_____

_____

_____

Live with Intention: My word of the day is _____.

Reflection

As I think about my thoughts, feelings and actions, what feels satisfying in my world? How am I aligning my purpose, passion, projects and performance to help me achieve my dreams?

_____

_____

_____

_____

_____

_____

_____

_____

_____

_____

_____

_____

_____

_____

_____

_____

_____

_____

_____

_____

Morning Messages

Vision: What feelings or experiences would you like to have had by the end of today?

_____

_____

_____

Motivation: What would my best self like to say to me today?

_____

_____

_____

Planning: What are my three priorities for today?

_____

_____

_____

Action: What is one small action I can take today that will bring me closer to my goals and dreams?

_____

_____

_____

Challenges: What obstacles, challenges, or mindset issues might I have to overcome today? What can I do to minimize them?

_____

_____

_____

Live with Intention: My word of the day is _____.

Reflection

As I think about my thoughts, feelings and actions, what feels satisfying in my world? How am I aligning my purpose, passion, projects and performance to help me achieve my dreams?

_____

_____

_____

_____

_____

_____

_____

_____

_____

_____

_____

_____

_____

_____

_____

_____

_____

_____

_____

_____

_____

_____

_____

_____

_____

Morning Messages

Vision: What feelings or experiences would you like to have had by the end of today?

_____

_____

_____

Motivation: What would my best self like to say to me today?

_____

_____

_____

Planning: What are my three priorities for today?

_____

_____

_____

Action: What is one small action I can take today that will bring me closer to my goals and dreams?

_____

_____

_____

Challenges: What obstacles, challenges, or mindset issues might I have to overcome today? What can I do to minimize them?

_____

_____

_____

Live with Intention: My word of the day is _____.

Reflection

As I think about my thoughts, feelings and actions, what feels satisfying in my world? How am I aligning my purpose, passion, projects and performance to help me achieve my dreams?

_____

_____

_____

_____

_____

_____

_____

_____

_____

_____

_____

_____

_____

_____

_____

_____

_____

_____

_____

_____

Morning Messages

Vision: What feelings or experiences would you like to have had by the end of today?

_____

_____

_____

Motivation: What would my best self like to say to me today?

_____

_____

_____

Planning: What are my three priorities for today?

_____

_____

_____

Action: What is one small action I can take today that will bring me closer to my goals and dreams?

_____

_____

_____

Challenges: What obstacles, challenges, or mindset issues might I have to overcome today? What can I do to minimize them?

_____

_____

_____

Live with Intention: My word of the day is _____.

Reflection

As I think about my thoughts, feelings and actions, what feels satisfying in my world? How am I aligning my purpose, passion, projects and performance to help me achieve my dreams?

_____

_____

_____

_____

_____

_____

_____

_____

_____

_____

_____

_____

_____

_____

_____

_____

_____

_____

_____

Morning Messages

Vision: What feelings or experiences would you like to have had by the end of today?

_____

_____

_____

Motivation: What would my best self like to say to me today?

_____

_____

_____

Planning: What are my three priorities for today?

_____

_____

_____

Action: What is one small action I can take today that will bring me closer to my goals and dreams?

_____

_____

_____

Challenges: What obstacles, challenges, or mindset issues might I have to overcome today? What can I do to minimize them?

_____

_____

_____

Live with Intention: My word of the day is _____.

Reflection

As I think about my thoughts, feelings and actions, what feels satisfying in my world? How am I aligning my purpose, passion, projects and performance to help me achieve my dreams?

_____

_____

_____

_____

_____

_____

_____

_____

_____

_____

_____

_____

_____

_____

_____

_____

_____

_____

_____

_____

Morning Messages

Vision: What feelings or experiences would you like to have had by the end of today?

_____

_____

_____

Motivation: What would my best self like to say to me today?

_____

_____

_____

Planning: What are my three priorities for today?

_____

_____

_____

Action: What is one small action I can take today that will bring me closer to my goals and dreams?

_____

_____

_____

Challenges: What obstacles, challenges, or mindset issues might I have to overcome today? What can I do to minimize them?

_____

_____

_____

Live with Intention: My word of the day is _____.

Reflection

As I think about my thoughts, feelings and actions, what feels satisfying in my world? How am I aligning my purpose, passion, projects and performance to help me achieve my dreams?

_____

_____

_____

_____

_____

_____

_____

_____

_____

_____

_____

_____

_____

_____

_____

_____

_____

_____

_____

_____

_____

Morning Messages

Vision: What feelings or experiences would you like to have had by the end of today?

_____

_____

_____

Motivation: What would my best self like to say to me today?

_____

_____

_____

Planning: What are my three priorities for today?

_____

_____

_____

Action: What is one small action I can take today that will bring me closer to my goals and dreams?

_____

_____

_____

Challenges: What obstacles, challenges, or mindset issues might I have to overcome today? What can I do to minimize them?

_____

_____

_____

Live with Intention: My word of the day is _____.

Reflection

As I think about my thoughts, feelings and actions, what feels satisfying in my world? How am I aligning my purpose, passion, projects and performance to help me achieve my dreams?

_____

_____

_____

_____

_____

_____

_____

_____

_____

_____

_____

_____

_____

_____

_____

_____

_____

_____

Morning Messages

Vision: What feelings or experiences would you like to have had by the end of today?

_____

_____

_____

Motivation: What would my best self like to say to me today?

_____

_____

_____

Planning: What are my three priorities for today?

_____

_____

_____

Action: What is one small action I can take today that will bring me closer to my goals and dreams?

_____

_____

_____

Challenges: What obstacles, challenges, or mindset issues might I have to overcome today? What can I do to minimize them?

_____

_____

_____

Live with Intention: My word of the day is _____.

Reflection

As I think about my thoughts, feelings and actions, what feels satisfying in my world? How am I aligning my purpose, passion, projects and performance to help me achieve my dreams?

_____

_____

_____

_____

_____

_____

_____

_____

_____

_____

_____

_____

_____

_____

_____

_____

_____

_____

_____

Morning Messages

Vision: What feelings or experiences would you like to have had by the end of today?

_____

_____

_____

Motivation: What would my best self like to say to me today?

_____

_____

_____

Planning: What are my three priorities for today?

_____

_____

_____

Action: What is one small action I can take today that will bring me closer to my goals and dreams?

_____

_____

_____

Challenges: What obstacles, challenges, or mindset issues might I have to overcome today? What can I do to minimize them?

_____

_____

_____

Live with Intention: My word of the day is _____.

Reflection

As I think about my thoughts, feelings and actions, what feels satisfying in my world? How am I aligning my purpose, passion, projects and performance to help me achieve my dreams?

_____

_____

_____

_____

_____

_____

_____

_____

_____

_____

_____

_____

_____

_____

_____

_____

_____

_____

_____

_____

_____

_____

Morning Messages

Vision: What feelings or experiences would you like to have had by the end of today?

_____

_____

Motivation: What would my best self like to say to me today?

_____

_____

Planning: What are my three priorities for today?

_____

_____

Action: What is one small action I can take today that will bring me closer to my goals and dreams?

_____

_____

Challenges: What obstacles, challenges, or mindset issues might I have to overcome today? What can I do to minimize them?

_____

_____

_____

Live with Intention: My word of the day is _____.

Reflection

As I think about my thoughts, feelings and actions, what feels satisfying in my world? How am I aligning my purpose, passion, projects and performance to help me achieve my dreams?

_____

_____

_____

_____

_____

_____

_____

_____

_____

_____

_____

_____

_____

_____

_____

_____

_____

_____

_____

Morning Messages

Vision: What feelings or experiences would you like to have had by the end of today?

_____

_____

Motivation: What would my best self like to say to me today?

_____

_____

Planning: What are my three priorities for today?

_____

_____

Action: What is one small action I can take today that will bring me closer to my goals and dreams?

_____

_____

Challenges: What obstacles, challenges, or mindset issues might I have to overcome today? What can I do to minimize them?

_____

_____

_____

Live with Intention: My word of the day is _____.

Reflection

As I think about my thoughts, feelings and actions, what feels satisfying in my world? How am I aligning my purpose, passion, projects and performance to help me achieve my dreams?

_____

_____

_____

_____

_____

_____

_____

_____

_____

_____

_____

_____

_____

_____

_____

_____

_____

_____

_____

_____

_____

Morning Messages

Vision: What feelings or experiences would you like to have had by the end of today?

_____

_____

_____

Motivation: What would my best self like to say to me today?

_____

_____

_____

Planning: What are my three priorities for today?

_____

_____

_____

Action: What is one small action I can take today that will bring me closer to my goals and dreams?

_____

_____

_____

Challenges: What obstacles, challenges, or mindset issues might I have to overcome today? What can I do to minimize them?

_____

_____

_____

Live with Intention: My word of the day is _____.

Reflection

As I think about my thoughts, feelings and actions, what feels satisfying in my world? How am I aligning my purpose, passion, projects and performance to help me achieve my dreams?

_____

_____

_____

_____

_____

_____

_____

_____

_____

_____

_____

_____

_____

_____

_____

_____

_____

_____

_____

_____

Morning Messages

Vision: What feelings or experiences would you like to have had by the end of today?

_____

_____

_____

Motivation: What would my best self like to say to me today?

_____

_____

_____

Planning: What are my three priorities for today?

_____

_____

_____

Action: What is one small action I can take today that will bring me closer to my goals and dreams?

_____

_____

_____

Challenges: What obstacles, challenges, or mindset issues might I have to overcome today? What can I do to minimize them?

_____

_____

_____

Live with Intention: My word of the day is _____.

Reflection

As I think about my thoughts, feelings and actions, what feels satisfying in my world? How am I aligning my purpose, passion, projects and performance to help me achieve my dreams?

_____

_____

_____

_____

_____

_____

_____

_____

_____

_____

_____

_____

_____

_____

_____

_____

Morning Messages

Vision: What feelings or experiences would you like to have had by the end of today?

_____

_____

_____

Motivation: What would my best self like to say to me today?

_____

_____

_____

Planning: What are my three priorities for today?

_____

_____

_____

Action: What is one small action I can take today that will bring me closer to my goals and dreams?

_____

_____

_____

Challenges: What obstacles, challenges, or mindset issues might I have to overcome today? What can I do to minimize them?

_____

_____

_____

Live with Intention: My word of the day is _____.

Reflection

As I think about my thoughts, feelings and actions, what feels satisfying in my world? How am I aligning my purpose, passion, projects and performance to help me achieve my dreams?

_____

_____

_____

_____

_____

_____

_____

_____

_____

_____

_____

_____

_____

_____

_____

_____

_____

_____

Morning Messages

Vision: What feelings or experiences would you like to have had by the end of today?

_____

_____

_____

Motivation: What would my best self like to say to me today?

_____

_____

_____

Planning: What are my three priorities for today?

_____

_____

_____

Action: What is one small action I can take today that will bring me closer to my goals and dreams?

_____

_____

_____

Challenges: What obstacles, challenges, or mindset issues might I have to overcome today? What can I do to minimize them?

_____

_____

_____

Live with Intention: My word of the day is _____.

Reflection

As I think about my thoughts, feelings and actions, what feels satisfying in my world? How am I aligning my purpose, passion, projects and performance to help me achieve my dreams?

_____

_____

_____

_____

_____

_____

_____

_____

_____

_____

_____

_____

_____

_____

_____

_____

_____

_____

_____

_____

Morning Messages

Vision: What feelings or experiences would you like to have had by the end of today?

_____

_____

_____

Motivation: What would my best self like to say to me today?

_____

_____

_____

Planning: What are my three priorities for today?

_____

_____

_____

Action: What is one small action I can take today that will bring me closer to my goals and dreams?

_____

_____

_____

Challenges: What obstacles, challenges, or mindset issues might I have to overcome today? What can I do to minimize them?

_____

_____

_____

Live with Intention: My word of the day is _____.

Reflection

As I think about my thoughts, feelings and actions, what feels satisfying in my world? How am I aligning my purpose, passion, projects and performance to help me achieve my dreams?

_____

_____

_____

_____

_____

_____

_____

_____

_____

_____

_____

_____

_____

_____

_____

_____

_____

_____

_____

Morning Messages

Vision: What feelings or experiences would you like to have had by the end of today?

_____

_____

_____

Motivation: What would my best self like to say to me today?

_____

_____

_____

Planning: What are my three priorities for today?

_____

_____

_____

Action: What is one small action I can take today that will bring me closer to my goals and dreams?

_____

_____

_____

Challenges: What obstacles, challenges, or mindset issues might I have to overcome today? What can I do to minimize them?

_____

_____

_____

Live with Intention: My word of the day is _____.

Reflection

As I think about my thoughts, feelings and actions, what feels satisfying in my world? How am I aligning my purpose, passion, projects and performance to help me achieve my dreams?

_____

_____

_____

_____

_____

_____

_____

_____

_____

_____

_____

_____

_____

_____

_____

_____

_____

_____

_____

_____

Morning Messages

Vision: What feelings or experiences would you like to have had by the end of today?

_____

_____

_____

Motivation: What would my best self like to say to me today?

_____

_____

_____

Planning: What are my three priorities for today?

_____

_____

_____

Action: What is one small action I can take today that will bring me closer to my goals and dreams?

_____

_____

_____

Challenges: What obstacles, challenges, or mindset issues might I have to overcome today? What can I do to minimize them?

_____

_____

_____

Live with Intention: My word of the day is _____.

Reflection

As I think about my thoughts, feelings and actions, what feels satisfying in my world? How am I aligning my purpose, passion, projects and performance to help me achieve my dreams?

_____

_____

_____

_____

_____

_____

_____

_____

_____

_____

_____

_____

_____

_____

_____

_____

_____

_____

_____

_____

Morning Messages

Vision: What feelings or experiences would you like to have had by the end of today?

_____

_____

_____

Motivation: What would my best self like to say to me today?

_____

_____

_____

Planning: What are my three priorities for today?

_____

_____

_____

Action: What is one small action I can take today that will bring me closer to my goals and dreams?

_____

_____

_____

Challenges: What obstacles, challenges, or mindset issues might I have to overcome today? What can I do to minimize them?

_____

_____

_____

Live with Intention: My word of the day is _____.

Reflection

As I think about my thoughts, feelings and actions, what feels satisfying in my world? How am I aligning my purpose, passion, projects and performance to help me achieve my dreams?

_____

_____

_____

_____

_____

_____

_____

_____

_____

_____

_____

_____

_____

_____

_____

_____

_____

_____

_____

Morning Messages

Vision: What feelings or experiences would you like to have had by the end of today?

_____

_____

_____

Motivation: What would my best self like to say to me today?

_____

_____

_____

Planning: What are my three priorities for today?

_____

_____

_____

Action: What is one small action I can take today that will bring me closer to my goals and dreams?

_____

_____

_____

Challenges: What obstacles, challenges, or mindset issues might I have to overcome today? What can I do to minimize them?

_____

_____

_____

Live with Intention: My word of the day is _____.

Reflection

As I think about my thoughts, feelings and actions, what feels satisfying in my world? How am I aligning my purpose, passion, projects and performance to help me achieve my dreams?

_____

_____

_____

_____

_____

_____

_____

_____

_____

_____

_____

_____

_____

_____

_____

_____

_____

_____

_____

Morning Messages

Vision: What feelings or experiences would you like to have had by the end of today?

_____

_____

Motivation: What would my best self like to say to me today?

_____

_____

Planning: What are my three priorities for today?

_____

_____

Action: What is one small action I can take today that will bring me closer to my goals and dreams?

_____

_____

Challenges: What obstacles, challenges, or mindset issues might I have to overcome today? What can I do to minimize them?

_____

_____

_____

Live with Intention: My word of the day is _____.

Reflection

As I think about my thoughts, feelings and actions, what feels satisfying in my world? How am I aligning my purpose, passion, projects and performance to help me achieve my dreams?

_____

_____

_____

_____

_____

_____

_____

_____

_____

_____

_____

_____

_____

_____

_____

_____

_____

_____

Morning Messages

Vision: What feelings or experiences would you like to have had by the end of today?

_____

_____

_____

Motivation: What would my best self like to say to me today?

_____

_____

_____

Planning: What are my three priorities for today?

_____

_____

_____

Action: What is one small action I can take today that will bring me closer to my goals and dreams?

_____

_____

_____

Challenges: What obstacles, challenges, or mindset issues might I have to overcome today? What can I do to minimize them?

_____

_____

_____

Live with Intention: My word of the day is _____.

Reflection

As I think about my thoughts, feelings and actions, what feels satisfying in my world? How am I aligning my purpose, passion, projects and performance to help me achieve my dreams?

_____

_____

_____

_____

_____

_____

_____

_____

_____

_____

_____

_____

_____

_____

_____

_____

_____

_____

_____

_____

Morning Messages

Vision: What feelings or experiences would you like to have had by the end of today?

_____

_____

_____

Motivation: What would my best self like to say to me today?

_____

_____

_____

Planning: What are my three priorities for today?

_____

_____

_____

Action: What is one small action I can take today that will bring me closer to my goals and dreams?

_____

_____

_____

Challenges: What obstacles, challenges, or mindset issues might I have to overcome today? What can I do to minimize them?

_____

_____

_____

Live with Intention: My word of the day is _____.

Reflection

As I think about my thoughts, feelings and actions, what feels satisfying in my world? How am I aligning my purpose, passion, projects and performance to help me achieve my dreams?

_____

_____

_____

_____

_____

_____

_____

_____

_____

_____

_____

_____

_____

_____

_____

_____

_____

_____

_____

Morning Messages

Vision: What feelings or experiences would you like to have had by the end of today?

_____

_____

_____

Motivation: What would my best self like to say to me today?

_____

_____

_____

Planning: What are my three priorities for today?

_____

_____

_____

Action: What is one small action I can take today that will bring me closer to my goals and dreams?

_____

_____

_____

Challenges: What obstacles, challenges, or mindset issues might I have to overcome today? What can I do to minimize them?

_____

_____

_____

Live with Intention: My word of the day is _____.

Reflection

As I think about my thoughts, feelings and actions, what feels satisfying in my world? How am I aligning my purpose, passion, projects and performance to help me achieve my dreams?

Morning Messages

Vision: What feelings or experiences would you like to have had by the end of today?

_____

_____

_____

Motivation: What would my best self like to say to me today?

_____

_____

_____

Planning: What are my three priorities for today?

_____

_____

_____

Action: What is one small action I can take today that will bring me closer to my goals and dreams?

_____

_____

_____

Challenges: What obstacles, challenges, or mindset issues might I have to overcome today? What can I do to minimize them?

_____

_____

_____

Live with Intention: My word of the day is _____.

Reflection

As I think about my thoughts, feelings and actions, what feels satisfying in my world? How am I aligning my purpose, passion, projects and performance to help me achieve my dreams?

_____

_____

_____

_____

_____

_____

_____

_____

_____

_____

_____

_____

_____

_____

_____

_____

_____

_____

Morning Messages

Vision: What feelings or experiences would you like to have had by the end of today?

_____

_____

_____

Motivation: What would my best self like to say to me today?

_____

_____

_____

Planning: What are my three priorities for today?

_____

_____

_____

Action: What is one small action I can take today that will bring me closer to my goals and dreams?

_____

_____

_____

Challenges: What obstacles, challenges, or mindset issues might I have to overcome today? What can I do to minimize them?

_____

_____

_____

Live with Intention: My word of the day is _____.

Reflection

As I think about my thoughts, feelings and actions, what feels satisfying in my world? How am I aligning my purpose, passion, projects and performance to help me achieve my dreams?

_____

_____

_____

_____

_____

_____

_____

_____

_____

_____

_____

_____

_____

_____

_____

_____

_____

_____

_____

_____

Morning Messages

Vision: What feelings or experiences would you like to have had by the end of today?

_____

_____

_____

Motivation: What would my best self like to say to me today?

_____

_____

_____

Planning: What are my three priorities for today?

_____

_____

_____

Action: What is one small action I can take today that will bring me closer to my goals and dreams?

_____

_____

_____

Challenges: What obstacles, challenges, or mindset issues might I have to overcome today? What can I do to minimize them?

_____

_____

_____

Live with Intention: My word of the day is _____.

Reflection

As I think about my thoughts, feelings and actions, what feels satisfying in my world? How am I aligning my purpose, passion, projects and performance to help me achieve my dreams?

_____

_____

_____

_____

_____

_____

_____

_____

_____

_____

_____

_____

_____

_____

_____

_____

_____

_____

_____

Morning Messages

Vision: What feelings or experiences would you like to have had by the end of today?

_____

_____

_____

Motivation: What would my best self like to say to me today?

_____

_____

_____

Planning: What are my three priorities for today?

_____

_____

_____

Action: What is one small action I can take today that will bring me closer to my goals and dreams?

_____

_____

_____

Challenges: What obstacles, challenges, or mindset issues might I have to overcome today? What can I do to minimize them?

_____

_____

_____

Live with Intention: My word of the day is _____.

Reflection

As I think about my thoughts, feelings and actions, what feels satisfying in my world? How am I aligning my purpose, passion, projects and performance to help me achieve my dreams?

_____

_____

_____

_____

_____

_____

_____

_____

_____

_____

_____

_____

_____

_____

_____

_____

_____

_____

_____

_____

Morning Messages

Vision: What feelings or experiences would you like to have had by the end of today?

_____

_____

_____

Motivation: What would my best self like to say to me today?

_____

_____

_____

Planning: What are my three priorities for today?

_____

_____

_____

Action: What is one small action I can take today that will bring me closer to my goals and dreams?

_____

_____

_____

Challenges: What obstacles, challenges, or mindset issues might I have to overcome today? What can I do to minimize them?

_____

_____

_____

Live with Intention: My word of the day is _____.

Reflection

As I think about my thoughts, feelings and actions, what feels satisfying in my world? How am I aligning my purpose, passion, projects and performance to help me achieve my dreams?

_____

_____

_____

_____

_____

_____

_____

_____

_____

_____

_____

_____

_____

_____

_____

_____

_____

_____

_____

_____

_____

Morning Messages

Vision: What feelings or experiences would you like to have had by the end of today?

_____

_____

_____

Motivation: What would my best self like to say to me today?

_____

_____

_____

Planning: What are my three priorities for today?

_____

_____

_____

Action: What is one small action I can take today that will bring me closer to my goals and dreams?

_____

_____

_____

Challenges: What obstacles, challenges, or mindset issues might I have to overcome today? What can I do to minimize them?

_____

_____

_____

Live with Intention: My word of the day is _____.

Reflection

As I think about my thoughts, feelings and actions, what feels satisfying in my world? How am I aligning my purpose, passion, projects and performance to help me achieve my dreams?

_____

_____

_____

_____

_____

_____

_____

_____

_____

_____

_____

_____

_____

_____

_____

_____

_____

_____

_____

_____

Morning Messages

Vision: What feelings or experiences would you like to have had by the end of today?

_____

_____

_____

Motivation: What would my best self like to say to me today?

_____

_____

_____

Planning: What are my three priorities for today?

_____

_____

_____

Action: What is one small action I can take today that will bring me closer to my goals and dreams?

_____

_____

_____

Challenges: What obstacles, challenges, or mindset issues might I have to overcome today? What can I do to minimize them?

_____

_____

_____

Live with Intention: My word of the day is _____.

Reflection

As I think about my thoughts, feelings and actions, what feels satisfying in my world? How am I aligning my purpose, passion, projects and performance to help me achieve my dreams?

_____

_____

_____

_____

_____

_____

_____

_____

_____

_____

_____

_____

_____

_____

_____

_____

_____

_____

Morning Messages

Vision: What feelings or experiences would you like to have had by the end of today?

_____

_____

_____

Motivation: What would my best self like to say to me today?

_____

_____

_____

Planning: What are my three priorities for today?

_____

_____

_____

Action: What is one small action I can take today that will bring me closer to my goals and dreams?

_____

_____

_____

Challenges: What obstacles, challenges, or mindset issues might I have to overcome today? What can I do to minimize them?

_____

_____

_____

Live with Intention: My word of the day is _____.

Reflection

As I think about my thoughts, feelings and actions, what feels satisfying in my world? How am I aligning my purpose, passion, projects and performance to help me achieve my dreams?

_____

_____

_____

_____

_____

_____

_____

_____

_____

_____

_____

_____

_____

_____

_____

_____

_____

_____

_____

_____

Morning Messages

Vision: What feelings or experiences would you like to have had by the end of today?

_____

_____

_____

Motivation: What would my best self like to say to me today?

_____

_____

_____

Planning: What are my three priorities for today?

_____

_____

_____

Action: What is one small action I can take today that will bring me closer to my goals and dreams?

_____

_____

_____

Challenges: What obstacles, challenges, or mindset issues might I have to overcome today? What can I do to minimize them?

_____

_____

_____

Live with Intention: My word of the day is _____.

Reflection

As I think about my thoughts, feelings and actions, what feels satisfying in my world? How am I aligning my purpose, passion, projects and performance to help me achieve my dreams?

_____

_____

_____

_____

_____

_____

_____

_____

_____

_____

_____

_____

_____

_____

_____

_____

_____

_____

_____

_____

_____

_____

Morning Messages

Vision: What feelings or experiences would you like to have had by the end of today?

_____

_____

_____

Motivation: What would my best self like to say to me today?

_____

_____

_____

Planning: What are my three priorities for today?

_____

_____

_____

Action: What is one small action I can take today that will bring me closer to my goals and dreams?

_____

_____

_____

Challenges: What obstacles, challenges, or mindset issues might I have to overcome today? What can I do to minimize them?

_____

_____

_____

Live with Intention: My word of the day is _____.

Reflection

As I think about my thoughts, feelings and actions, what feels satisfying in my world? How am I aligning my purpose, passion, projects and performance to help me achieve my dreams?

_____

_____

_____

_____

_____

_____

_____

_____

_____

_____

_____

_____

_____

_____

_____

_____

_____

_____

_____

_____

Morning Messages

Vision: What feelings or experiences would you like to have had by the end of today?

_____

_____

_____

Motivation: What would my best self like to say to me today?

_____

_____

_____

Planning: What are my three priorities for today?

_____

_____

_____

Action: What is one small action I can take today that will bring me closer to my goals and dreams?

_____

_____

_____

Challenges: What obstacles, challenges, or mindset issues might I have to overcome today? What can I do to minimize them?

_____

_____

_____

Live with Intention: My word of the day is _____.

Reflection

As I think about my thoughts, feelings and actions, what feels satisfying in my world? How am I aligning my purpose, passion, projects and performance to help me achieve my dreams?

_____

_____

_____

_____

_____

_____

_____

_____

_____

_____

_____

_____

_____

_____

_____

_____

_____

_____

_____

_____

Morning Messages

Vision: What feelings or experiences would you like to have had by the end of today?

_____

_____

_____

Motivation: What would my best self like to say to me today?

_____

_____

_____

Planning: What are my three priorities for today?

_____

_____

_____

Action: What is one small action I can take today that will bring me closer to my goals and dreams?

_____

_____

_____

Challenges: What obstacles, challenges, or mindset issues might I have to overcome today? What can I do to minimize them?

_____

_____

_____

Live with Intention: My word of the day is _____.

Reflection

As I think about my thoughts, feelings and actions, what feels satisfying in my world? How am I aligning my purpose, passion, projects and performance to help me achieve my dreams?

_____

_____

_____

_____

_____

_____

_____

_____

_____

_____

_____

_____

_____

_____

_____

_____

_____

_____

_____

_____

_____

_____

Morning Messages

Vision: What feelings or experiences would you like to have had by the end of today?

_____

_____

_____

Motivation: What would my best self like to say to me today?

_____

_____

_____

Planning: What are my three priorities for today?

_____

_____

_____

Action: What is one small action I can take today that will bring me closer to my goals and dreams?

_____

_____

_____

Challenges: What obstacles, challenges, or mindset issues might I have to overcome today? What can I do to minimize them?

_____

_____

_____

Live with Intention: My word of the day is _____.

Reflection

As I think about my thoughts, feelings and actions, what feels satisfying in my world? How am I aligning my purpose, passion, projects and performance to help me achieve my dreams?

_____

_____

_____

_____

_____

_____

_____

_____

_____

_____

_____

_____

_____

_____

_____

_____

_____

_____

Morning Messages

Vision: What feelings or experiences would you like to have had by the end of today?

_____

_____

_____

Motivation: What would my best self like to say to me today?

_____

_____

_____

Planning: What are my three priorities for today?

_____

_____

_____

Action: What is one small action I can take today that will bring me closer to my goals and dreams?

_____

_____

_____

Challenges: What obstacles, challenges, or mindset issues might I have to overcome today? What can I do to minimize them?

_____

_____

_____

Live with Intention: My word of the day is _____.

Reflection

As I think about my thoughts, feelings and actions, what feels satisfying in my world? How am I aligning my purpose, passion, projects and performance to help me achieve my dreams?

_____

_____

_____

_____

_____

_____

_____

_____

_____

_____

_____

_____

_____

_____

_____

_____

_____

_____

_____

_____

Morning Messages

Vision: What feelings or experiences would you like to have had by the end of today?

_____

_____

_____

Motivation: What would my best self like to say to me today?

_____

_____

_____

Planning: What are my three priorities for today?

_____

_____

_____

Action: What is one small action I can take today that will bring me closer to my goals and dreams?

_____

_____

_____

Challenges: What obstacles, challenges, or mindset issues might I have to overcome today? What can I do to minimize them?

_____

_____

_____

Live with Intention: My word of the day is _____.

Reflection

As I think about my thoughts, feelings and actions, what feels satisfying in my world? How am I aligning my purpose, passion, projects and performance to help me achieve my dreams?

Morning Messages

Vision: What feelings or experiences would you like to have had by the end of today?

_____

_____

_____

Motivation: What would my best self like to say to me today?

_____

_____

_____

Planning: What are my three priorities for today?

_____

_____

_____

Action: What is one small action I can take today that will bring me closer to my goals and dreams?

_____

_____

_____

Challenges: What obstacles, challenges, or mindset issues might I have to overcome today? What can I do to minimize them?

_____

_____

_____

Live with Intention: My word of the day is _____.

Reflection

As I think about my thoughts, feelings and actions, what feels satisfying in my world? How am I aligning my purpose, passion, projects and performance to help me achieve my dreams?

_____

_____

_____

_____

_____

_____

_____

_____

_____

_____

_____

_____

_____

_____

_____

_____

_____

Morning Messages

Vision: What feelings or experiences would you like to have had by the end of today?

_____

_____

_____

Motivation: What would my best self like to say to me today?

_____

_____

_____

Planning: What are my three priorities for today?

_____

_____

_____

Action: What is one small action I can take today that will bring me closer to my goals and dreams?

_____

_____

_____

Challenges: What obstacles, challenges, or mindset issues might I have to overcome today? What can I do to minimize them?

_____

_____

_____

Live with Intention: My word of the day is _____.

Reflection

As I think about my thoughts, feelings and actions, what feels satisfying in my world? How am I aligning my purpose, passion, projects and performance to help me achieve my dreams?

_____

_____

_____

_____

_____

_____

_____

_____

_____

_____

_____

_____

_____

_____

_____

_____

_____

_____

_____

Morning Messages

Vision: What feelings or experiences would you like to have had by the end of today?

_____

_____

_____

Motivation: What would my best self like to say to me today?

_____

_____

_____

Planning: What are my three priorities for today?

_____

_____

_____

Action: What is one small action I can take today that will bring me closer to my goals and dreams?

_____

_____

_____

Challenges: What obstacles, challenges, or mindset issues might I have to overcome today? What can I do to minimize them?

_____

_____

_____

Live with Intention: My word of the day is _____.

Reflection

As I think about my thoughts, feelings and actions, what feels satisfying in my world? How am I aligning my purpose, passion, projects and performance to help me achieve my dreams?

_____

_____

_____

_____

_____

_____

_____

_____

_____

_____

_____

_____

_____

_____

_____

_____

_____

_____

_____

_____

Morning Messages

Vision: What feelings or experiences would you like to have had by the end of today?

_____

_____

_____

Motivation: What would my best self like to say to me today?

_____

_____

_____

Planning: What are my three priorities for today?

_____

_____

_____

Action: What is one small action I can take today that will bring me closer to my goals and dreams?

_____

_____

_____

Challenges: What obstacles, challenges, or mindset issues might I have to overcome today? What can I do to minimize them?

_____

_____

_____

Live with Intention: My word of the day is _____.

Reflection

As I think about my thoughts, feelings and actions, what feels satisfying in my world? How am I aligning my purpose, passion, projects and performance to help me achieve my dreams?

_____

_____

_____

_____

_____

_____

_____

_____

_____

_____

_____

_____

_____

_____

_____

_____

_____

_____

_____

Morning Messages

Vision: What feelings or experiences would you like to have had by the end of today?

_____

_____

_____

Motivation: What would my best self like to say to me today?

_____

_____

_____

Planning: What are my three priorities for today?

_____

_____

_____

Action: What is one small action I can take today that will bring me closer to my goals and dreams?

_____

_____

_____

Challenges: What obstacles, challenges, or mindset issues might I have to overcome today? What can I do to minimize them?

_____

_____

_____

Live with Intention: My word of the day is _____.

Reflection

As I think about my thoughts, feelings and actions, what feels satisfying in my world? How am I aligning my purpose, passion, projects and performance to help me achieve my dreams?

_____

_____

_____

_____

_____

_____

_____

_____

_____

_____

_____

_____

_____

_____

_____

_____

_____

_____

_____

Morning Messages

Vision: What feelings or experiences would you like to have had by the end of today?

_____

_____

_____

Motivation: What would my best self like to say to me today?

_____

_____

_____

Planning: What are my three priorities for today?

_____

_____

_____

Action: What is one small action I can take today that will bring me closer to my goals and dreams?

_____

_____

_____

Challenges: What obstacles, challenges, or mindset issues might I have to overcome today? What can I do to minimize them?

_____

_____

_____

Live with Intention: My word of the day is _____.

Reflection

As I think about my thoughts, feelings and actions, what feels satisfying in my world? How am I aligning my purpose, passion, projects and performance to help me achieve my dreams?

_____

_____

_____

_____

_____

_____

_____

_____

_____

_____

_____

_____

_____

_____

_____

_____

_____

_____

Morning Messages

Vision: What feelings or experiences would you like to have had by the end of today?

_____

_____

_____

Motivation: What would my best self like to say to me today?

_____

_____

_____

Planning: What are my three priorities for today?

_____

_____

_____

Action: What is one small action I can take today that will bring me closer to my goals and dreams?

_____

_____

_____

Challenges: What obstacles, challenges, or mindset issues might I have to overcome today? What can I do to minimize them?

_____

_____

_____

Live with Intention: My word of the day is _____.

Reflection

As I think about my thoughts, feelings and actions, what feels satisfying in my world? How am I aligning my purpose, passion, projects and performance to help me achieve my dreams?

_____

_____

_____

_____

_____

_____

_____

_____

_____

_____

_____

_____

_____

_____

_____

_____

_____

_____

_____

_____

Morning Messages

Vision: What feelings or experiences would you like to have had by the end of today?

_____

_____

_____

Motivation: What would my best self like to say to me today?

_____

_____

_____

Planning: What are my three priorities for today?

_____

_____

_____

Action: What is one small action I can take today that will bring me closer to my goals and dreams?

_____

_____

_____

Challenges: What obstacles, challenges, or mindset issues might I have to overcome today? What can I do to minimize them?

_____

_____

_____

Live with Intention: My word of the day is _____.

Reflection

As I think about my thoughts, feelings and actions, what feels satisfying in my world? How am I aligning my purpose, passion, projects and performance to help me achieve my dreams?

_____

_____

_____

_____

_____

_____

_____

_____

_____

_____

_____

_____

_____

_____

_____

_____

_____

_____

Morning Messages

Vision: What feelings or experiences would you like to have had by the end of today?

_____

_____

_____

Motivation: What would my best self like to say to me today?

_____

_____

_____

Planning: What are my three priorities for today?

_____

_____

_____

Action: What is one small action I can take today that will bring me closer to my goals and dreams?

_____

_____

_____

Challenges: What obstacles, challenges, or mindset issues might I have to overcome today? What can I do to minimize them?

_____

_____

_____

Live with Intention: My word of the day is _____.

Reflection

As I think about my thoughts, feelings and actions, what feels satisfying in my world? How am I aligning my purpose, passion, projects and performance to help me achieve my dreams?

_____

_____

_____

_____

_____

_____

_____

_____

_____

_____

_____

_____

_____

_____

_____

_____

_____

_____

_____

_____

_____

Morning Messages

Vision: What feelings or experiences would you like to have had by the end of today?

_____

_____

_____

Motivation: What would my best self like to say to me today?

_____

_____

_____

Planning: What are my three priorities for today?

_____

_____

_____

Action: What is one small action I can take today that will bring me closer to my goals and dreams?

_____

_____

_____

Challenges: What obstacles, challenges, or mindset issues might I have to overcome today? What can I do to minimize them?

_____

_____

_____

Live with Intention: My word of the day is _____.

Reflection

As I think about my thoughts, feelings and actions, what feels satisfying in my world? How am I aligning my purpose, passion, projects and performance to help me achieve my dreams?

_____

_____

_____

_____

_____

_____

_____

_____

_____

_____

_____

_____

_____

_____

_____

_____

_____

_____

Morning Messages

Vision: What feelings or experiences would you like to have had by the end of today?

_____

_____

_____

Motivation: What would my best self like to say to me today?

_____

_____

_____

Planning: What are my three priorities for today?

_____

_____

_____

Action: What is one small action I can take today that will bring me closer to my goals and dreams?

_____

_____

_____

Challenges: What obstacles, challenges, or mindset issues might I have to overcome today? What can I do to minimize them?

_____

_____

_____

Live with Intention: My word of the day is _____.

Reflection

As I think about my thoughts, feelings and actions, what feels satisfying in my world? How am I aligning my purpose, passion, projects and performance to help me achieve my dreams?

_____

_____

_____

_____

_____

_____

_____

_____

_____

_____

_____

_____

_____

_____

_____

_____

_____

_____

Morning Messages

Vision: What feelings or experiences would you like to have had by the end of today?

_____

_____

_____

Motivation: What would my best self like to say to me today?

_____

_____

_____

Planning: What are my three priorities for today?

_____

_____

_____

Action: What is one small action I can take today that will bring me closer to my goals and dreams?

_____

_____

_____

Challenges: What obstacles, challenges, or mindset issues might I have to overcome today? What can I do to minimize them?

_____

_____

_____

Live with Intention: My word of the day is _____.

Reflection

As I think about my thoughts, feelings and actions, what feels satisfying in my world? How am I aligning my purpose, passion, projects and performance to help me achieve my dreams?

_____

_____

_____

_____

_____

_____

_____

_____

_____

_____

_____

_____

_____

_____

_____

_____

_____

Morning Messages

Vision: What feelings or experiences would you like to have had by the end of today?

_____

_____

_____

Motivation: What would my best self like to say to me today?

_____

_____

_____

Planning: What are my three priorities for today?

_____

_____

_____

Action: What is one small action I can take today that will bring me closer to my goals and dreams?

_____

_____

_____

Challenges: What obstacles, challenges, or mindset issues might I have to overcome today? What can I do to minimize them?

_____

_____

_____

Live with Intention: My word of the day is _____.

Reflection

As I think about my thoughts, feelings and actions, what feels satisfying in my world? How am I aligning my purpose, passion, projects and performance to help me achieve my dreams?

_____

_____

_____

_____

_____

_____

_____

_____

_____

_____

_____

_____

_____

_____

_____

_____

_____

_____

_____

Morning Messages

Vision: What feelings or experiences would you like to have had by the end of today?

_____

_____

_____

Motivation: What would my best self like to say to me today?

_____

_____

_____

Planning: What are my three priorities for today?

_____

_____

_____

Action: What is one small action I can take today that will bring me closer to my goals and dreams?

_____

_____

_____

Challenges: What obstacles, challenges, or mindset issues might I have to overcome today? What can I do to minimize them?

_____

_____

_____

Live with Intention: My word of the day is _____.

Reflection

As I think about my thoughts, feelings and actions, what feels satisfying in my world? How am I aligning my purpose, passion, projects and performance to help me achieve my dreams?

_____

_____

_____

_____

_____

_____

_____

_____

_____

_____

_____

_____

_____

_____

_____

_____

_____

_____

_____

_____

Morning Messages

Vision: What feelings or experiences would you like to have had by the end of today?

_____

_____

_____

Motivation: What would my best self like to say to me today?

_____

_____

_____

Planning: What are my three priorities for today?

_____

_____

_____

Action: What is one small action I can take today that will bring me closer to my goals and dreams?

_____

_____

_____

Challenges: What obstacles, challenges, or mindset issues might I have to overcome today? What can I do to minimize them?

_____

_____

_____

Live with Intention: My word of the day is _____.

Reflection

As I think about my thoughts, feelings and actions, what feels satisfying in my world? How am I aligning my purpose, passion, projects and performance to help me achieve my dreams?

Morning Messages

Vision: What feelings or experiences would you like to have had by the end of today?

_____

_____

_____

Motivation: What would my best self like to say to me today?

_____

_____

_____

Planning: What are my three priorities for today?

_____

_____

_____

Action: What is one small action I can take today that will bring me closer to my goals and dreams?

_____

_____

_____

Challenges: What obstacles, challenges, or mindset issues might I have to overcome today? What can I do to minimize them?

_____

_____

_____

Live with Intention: My word of the day is _____.

Reflection

As I think about my thoughts, feelings and actions, what feels satisfying in my world? How am I aligning my purpose, passion, projects and performance to help me achieve my dreams?

_____

_____

_____

_____

_____

_____

_____

_____

_____

_____

_____

_____

_____

_____

_____

_____

_____

_____

Morning Messages

Vision: What feelings or experiences would you like to have had by the end of today?

_____

_____

_____

Motivation: What would my best self like to say to me today?

_____

_____

_____

Planning: What are my three priorities for today?

_____

_____

_____

Action: What is one small action I can take today that will bring me closer to my goals and dreams?

_____

_____

_____

Challenges: What obstacles, challenges, or mindset issues might I have to overcome today? What can I do to minimize them?

_____

_____

_____

Live with Intention: My word of the day is _____.

Reflection

As I think about my thoughts, feelings and actions, what feels satisfying in my world? How am I aligning my purpose, passion, projects and performance to help me achieve my dreams?

_____

_____

_____

_____

_____

_____

_____

_____

_____

_____

_____

_____

_____

_____

_____

_____

_____

_____

_____

Morning Messages

Vision: What feelings or experiences would you like to have had by the end of today?

_____

_____

_____

Motivation: What would my best self like to say to me today?

_____

_____

_____

Planning: What are my three priorities for today?

_____

_____

_____

Action: What is one small action I can take today that will bring me closer to my goals and dreams?

_____

_____

_____

Challenges: What obstacles, challenges, or mindset issues might I have to overcome today? What can I do to minimize them?

_____

_____

_____

Live with Intention: My word of the day is _____.

Reflection

As I think about my thoughts, feelings and actions, what feels satisfying in my world? How am I aligning my purpose, passion, projects and performance to help me achieve my dreams?

_____

_____

_____

_____

_____

_____

_____

_____

_____

_____

_____

_____

_____

_____

_____

_____

_____

_____

_____

_____

_____

_____

Morning Messages

Vision: What feelings or experiences would you like to have had by the end of today?

_____

_____

_____

Motivation: What would my best self like to say to me today?

_____

_____

_____

Planning: What are my three priorities for today?

_____

_____

_____

Action: What is one small action I can take today that will bring me closer to my goals and dreams?

_____

_____

_____

Challenges: What obstacles, challenges, or mindset issues might I have to overcome today? What can I do to minimize them?

_____

_____

_____

Live with Intention: My word of the day is _____.

Reflection

As I think about my thoughts, feelings and actions, what feels satisfying in my world? How am I aligning my purpose, passion, projects and performance to help me achieve my dreams?

_____

_____

_____

_____

_____

_____

_____

_____

_____

_____

_____

_____

_____

_____

_____

_____

_____

_____

Morning Messages

Vision: What feelings or experiences would you like to have had by the end of today?

_____

_____

_____

Motivation: What would my best self like to say to me today?

_____

_____

_____

Planning: What are my three priorities for today?

_____

_____

_____

Action: What is one small action I can take today that will bring me closer to my goals and dreams?

_____

_____

_____

Challenges: What obstacles, challenges, or mindset issues might I have to overcome today? What can I do to minimize them?

_____

_____

_____

Live with Intention: My word of the day is _____.

Reflection

As I think about my thoughts, feelings and actions, what feels satisfying in my world? How am I aligning my purpose, passion, projects and performance to help me achieve my dreams?

_____

_____

_____

_____

_____

_____

_____

_____

_____

_____

_____

_____

_____

_____

_____

_____

_____

_____

_____

Morning Messages

Vision: What feelings or experiences would you like to have had by the end of today?

_____

_____

Motivation: What would my best self like to say to me today?

_____

_____

Planning: What are my three priorities for today?

_____

_____

Action: What is one small action I can take today that will bring me closer to my goals and dreams?

_____

_____

Challenges: What obstacles, challenges, or mindset issues might I have to overcome today? What can I do to minimize them?

_____

_____

_____

Live with Intention: My word of the day is _____.

Reflection

As I think about my thoughts, feelings and actions, what feels satisfying in my world? How am I aligning my purpose, passion, projects and performance to help me achieve my dreams?

_____

_____

_____

_____

_____

_____

_____

_____

_____

_____

_____

_____

_____

_____

_____

_____

_____

_____

_____

Morning Messages

Vision: What feelings or experiences would you like to have had by the end of today?

_____

_____

_____

Motivation: What would my best self like to say to me today?

_____

_____

_____

Planning: What are my three priorities for today?

_____

_____

_____

Action: What is one small action I can take today that will bring me closer to my goals and dreams?

_____

_____

_____

Challenges: What obstacles, challenges, or mindset issues might I have to overcome today? What can I do to minimize them?

_____

_____

_____

Live with Intention: My word of the day is _____.

Reflection

As I think about my thoughts, feelings and actions, what feels satisfying in my world? How am I aligning my purpose, passion, projects and performance to help me achieve my dreams?

Morning Messages

Vision: What feelings or experiences would you like to have had by the end of today?

_____

_____

_____

Motivation: What would my best self like to say to me today?

_____

_____

_____

Planning: What are my three priorities for today?

_____

_____

_____

Action: What is one small action I can take today that will bring me closer to my goals and dreams?

_____

_____

_____

Challenges: What obstacles, challenges, or mindset issues might I have to overcome today? What can I do to minimize them?

_____

_____

_____

Live with Intention: My word of the day is _____.

Reflection

As I think about my thoughts, feelings and actions, what feels satisfying in my world? How am I aligning my purpose, passion, projects and performance to help me achieve my dreams?

_____

_____

_____

_____

_____

_____

_____

_____

_____

_____

_____

_____

_____

_____

_____

_____

_____

_____

_____

_____

_____

_____

Morning Messages

Vision: What feelings or experiences would you like to have had by the end of today?

_____

_____

_____

Motivation: What would my best self like to say to me today?

_____

_____

_____

Planning: What are my three priorities for today?

_____

_____

_____

Action: What is one small action I can take today that will bring me closer to my goals and dreams?

_____

_____

_____

Challenges: What obstacles, challenges, or mindset issues might I have to overcome today? What can I do to minimize them?

_____

_____

_____

Live with Intention: My word of the day is _____.

Reflection

As I think about my thoughts, feelings and actions, what feels satisfying in my world? How am I aligning my purpose, passion, projects and performance to help me achieve my dreams?

_____

_____

_____

_____

_____

_____

_____

_____

_____

_____

_____

_____

_____

_____

_____

_____

_____

_____

_____

Morning Messages

Vision: What feelings or experiences would you like to have had by the end of today?

_____

_____

_____

Motivation: What would my best self like to say to me today?

_____

_____

_____

Planning: What are my three priorities for today?

_____

_____

_____

Action: What is one small action I can take today that will bring me closer to my goals and dreams?

_____

_____

_____

Challenges: What obstacles, challenges, or mindset issues might I have to overcome today? What can I do to minimize them?

_____

_____

_____

Live with Intention: My word of the day is _____.

Reflection

As I think about my thoughts, feelings and actions, what feels satisfying in my world? How am I aligning my purpose, passion, projects and performance to help me achieve my dreams?

_____

_____

_____

_____

_____

_____

_____

_____

_____

_____

_____

_____

_____

_____

_____

_____

_____

_____

_____

_____

Morning Messages

Vision: What feelings or experiences would you like to have had by the end of today?

_____

_____

_____

Motivation: What would my best self like to say to me today?

_____

_____

_____

Planning: What are my three priorities for today?

_____

_____

_____

Action: What is one small action I can take today that will bring me closer to my goals and dreams?

_____

_____

_____

Challenges: What obstacles, challenges, or mindset issues might I have to overcome today? What can I do to minimize them?

_____

_____

_____

Live with Intention: My word of the day is _____.

Reflection

As I think about my thoughts, feelings and actions, what feels satisfying in my world? How am I aligning my purpose, passion, projects and performance to help me achieve my dreams?

_____

_____

_____

_____

_____

_____

_____

_____

_____

_____

_____

_____

_____

_____

_____

_____

_____

_____

_____

_____

Morning Messages

Vision: What feelings or experiences would you like to have had by the end of today?

_____

_____

_____

Motivation: What would my best self like to say to me today?

_____

_____

_____

Planning: What are my three priorities for today?

_____

_____

_____

Action: What is one small action I can take today that will bring me closer to my goals and dreams?

_____

_____

_____

Challenges: What obstacles, challenges, or mindset issues might I have to overcome today? What can I do to minimize them?

_____

_____

_____

Live with Intention: My word of the day is _____.

Reflection

As I think about my thoughts, feelings and actions, what feels satisfying in my world? How am I aligning my purpose, passion, projects and performance to help me achieve my dreams?

_____

_____

_____

_____

_____

_____

_____

_____

_____

_____

_____

_____

_____

_____

_____

_____

_____

_____

_____

_____

Morning Messages

Vision: What feelings or experiences would you like to have had by the end of today?

_____

_____

_____

Motivation: What would my best self like to say to me today?

_____

_____

_____

Planning: What are my three priorities for today?

_____

_____

_____

Action: What is one small action I can take today that will bring me closer to my goals and dreams?

_____

_____

_____

Challenges: What obstacles, challenges, or mindset issues might I have to overcome today? What can I do to minimize them?

_____

_____

_____

Live with Intention: My word of the day is _____.

Reflection

As I think about my thoughts, feelings and actions, what feels satisfying in my world? How am I aligning my purpose, passion, projects and performance to help me achieve my dreams?

_____

_____

_____

_____

_____

_____

_____

_____

_____

_____

_____

_____

_____

_____

_____

_____

_____

_____

_____

Morning Messages

Vision: What feelings or experiences would you like to have had by the end of today?

_____

_____

_____

Motivation: What would my best self like to say to me today?

_____

_____

_____

Planning: What are my three priorities for today?

_____

_____

_____

Action: What is one small action I can take today that will bring me closer to my goals and dreams?

_____

_____

_____

Challenges: What obstacles, challenges, or mindset issues might I have to overcome today? What can I do to minimize them?

_____

_____

_____

Live with Intention: My word of the day is _____.

Reflection

As I think about my thoughts, feelings and actions, what feels satisfying in my world? How am I aligning my purpose, passion, projects and performance to help me achieve my dreams?

Morning Messages

Vision: What feelings or experiences would you like to have had by the end of today?

_____

_____

_____

Motivation: What would my best self like to say to me today?

_____

_____

_____

Planning: What are my three priorities for today?

_____

_____

_____

Action: What is one small action I can take today that will bring me closer to my goals and dreams?

_____

_____

_____

Challenges: What obstacles, challenges, or mindset issues might I have to overcome today? What can I do to minimize them?

_____

_____

_____

Live with Intention: My word of the day is _____.

Reflection

As I think about my thoughts, feelings and actions, what feels satisfying in my world? How am I aligning my purpose, passion, projects and performance to help me achieve my dreams?

_____

_____

_____

_____

_____

_____

_____

_____

_____

_____

_____

_____

_____

_____

_____

_____

_____

Morning Messages

Vision: What feelings or experiences would you like to have had by the end of today?

_____

_____

_____

Motivation: What would my best self like to say to me today?

_____

_____

_____

Planning: What are my three priorities for today?

_____

_____

_____

Action: What is one small action I can take today that will bring me closer to my goals and dreams?

_____

_____

_____

Challenges: What obstacles, challenges, or mindset issues might I have to overcome today? What can I do to minimize them?

_____

_____

_____

Live with Intention: My word of the day is _____.

Reflection

As I think about my thoughts, feelings and actions, what feels satisfying in my world? How am I aligning my purpose, passion, projects and performance to help me achieve my dreams?

_____

_____

_____

_____

_____

_____

_____

_____

_____

_____

_____

_____

_____

_____

_____

_____

_____

_____

Morning Messages

Vision: What feelings or experiences would you like to have had by the end of today?

_____

_____

_____

Motivation: What would my best self like to say to me today?

_____

_____

_____

Planning: What are my three priorities for today?

_____

_____

_____

Action: What is one small action I can take today that will bring me closer to my goals and dreams?

_____

_____

_____

Challenges: What obstacles, challenges, or mindset issues might I have to overcome today? What can I do to minimize them?

_____

_____

_____

Live with Intention: My word of the day is _____.

Reflection

As I think about my thoughts, feelings and actions, what feels satisfying in my world? How am I aligning my purpose, passion, projects and performance to help me achieve my dreams?

_____

_____

_____

_____

_____

_____

_____

_____

_____

_____

_____

_____

_____

_____

_____

_____

_____

_____

_____

Morning Messages

Vision: What feelings or experiences would you like to have had by the end of today?

_____

_____

_____

Motivation: What would my best self like to say to me today?

_____

_____

_____

Planning: What are my three priorities for today?

_____

_____

_____

Action: What is one small action I can take today that will bring me closer to my goals and dreams?

_____

_____

_____

Challenges: What obstacles, challenges, or mindset issues might I have to overcome today? What can I do to minimize them?

_____

_____

_____

Live with Intention: My word of the day is _____.

Reflection

As I think about my thoughts, feelings and actions, what feels satisfying in my world? How am I aligning my purpose, passion, projects and performance to help me achieve my dreams?

_____

_____

_____

_____

_____

_____

_____

_____

_____

_____

_____

_____

_____

_____

_____

_____

_____

_____

Morning Messages

Vision: What feelings or experiences would you like to have had by the end of today?

_____

_____

_____

Motivation: What would my best self like to say to me today?

_____

_____

_____

Planning: What are my three priorities for today?

_____

_____

_____

Action: What is one small action I can take today that will bring me closer to my goals and dreams?

_____

_____

_____

Challenges: What obstacles, challenges, or mindset issues might I have to overcome today? What can I do to minimize them?

_____

_____

_____

Live with Intention: My word of the day is _____.

Reflection

As I think about my thoughts, feelings and actions, what feels satisfying in my world? How am I aligning my purpose, passion, projects and performance to help me achieve my dreams?

_____

_____

_____

_____

_____

_____

_____

_____

_____

_____

_____

_____

_____

_____

_____

_____

_____

_____

_____

Morning Messages

Vision: What feelings or experiences would you like to have had by the end of today?

_____

_____

_____

Motivation: What would my best self like to say to me today?

_____

_____

_____

Planning: What are my three priorities for today?

_____

_____

_____

Action: What is one small action I can take today that will bring me closer to my goals and dreams?

_____

_____

_____

Challenges: What obstacles, challenges, or mindset issues might I have to overcome today? What can I do to minimize them?

_____

_____

_____

Live with Intention: My word of the day is _____.

Reflection

As I think about my thoughts, feelings and actions, what feels satisfying in my world? How am I aligning my purpose, passion, projects and performance to help me achieve my dreams?

_____

_____

_____

_____

_____

_____

_____

_____

_____

_____

_____

_____

_____

_____

_____

_____

_____

_____

Morning Messages

Vision: What feelings or experiences would you like to have had by the end of today?

_____

_____

_____

Motivation: What would my best self like to say to me today?

_____

_____

_____

Planning: What are my three priorities for today?

_____

_____

_____

Action: What is one small action I can take today that will bring me closer to my goals and dreams?

_____

_____

_____

Challenges: What obstacles, challenges, or mindset issues might I have to overcome today? What can I do to minimize them?

_____

_____

_____

Live with Intention: My word of the day is _____.

Reflection

As I think about my thoughts, feelings and actions, what feels satisfying in my world? How am I aligning my purpose, passion, projects and performance to help me achieve my dreams?

About the Author

Michele Vosberg, Ph.D. is an award-winning educator, author, and international speaker. She has conducted workshops throughout the United States, Europe and South America.

Michele believes that we all have gifts and talents, and that the world is a better place when we use them to enhance our own lives and the lives of others. Michele's gift is seeing potential. She has used that gift in her life and career to help others discover and bring about their own best gifts. Bringing potential to life is her highest calling and most joyous work.

Michele lives in Madison, Wisconsin with her husband and two cats. She has two grown daughters.

You can find Michele on her website michelevosberg.com.

Made in the USA
Monee, IL
01 February 2022

90365754R00125